The Christmas Gift

THE STORY OF THE NATIVITY

Retold by
Elizabeth Laird

Illustrated by Bettina Paterson

Hippo

*For my father, Dudley
In memoriam*
B.P.

For Edvard
E.L.

Scholastic Children's Books
Commonwealth House, 1-19 New Oxford Street
London WC1A 1NU, UK
a division of Scholastic Ltd
London ~ New York ~ Toronto ~ Sydney ~ Auckland
Mexico City ~ New Delhi ~ Hong Kong

First published in hardback by Scholastic Ltd, 1998 as *Gabriel's Feather*
This paperback edition published by Scholastic Ltd, 2002

Text copyright © Elizabeth Laird, 1998
Illustrations copyright © Bettina Paterson, 1998

ISBN 0 439 98143 3

M ary was alone in her house,
baking loaves of bread.

She heard a flutter of wings, and looked up.
The angel Gabriel stood there.
"Don't be afraid, Mary," he said.

"I'm bringing you good news.
You're going to have a baby,
and he will be the Son of God."

Soon, Mary knew that the baby would be born.
She told her husband, Joseph.
"We'll care for him together," Joseph said.

A messenger came from Caesar Augustus.
"You must all go back to your own city,
to pay your taxes!" the messenger cried.

"Come, Mary," Joseph said.
"Our families used to live in Bethlehem.
 We must obey the law and go there now."

He saddled the donkey,
and Mary put some food in a bag,
and they set off down the road to Bethlehem.

There were crowds of people in the town.
Every house was full.
"Please give us a room," Joseph said to the innkeeper.
"My wife's going to have a baby. She needs to rest."

"All the rooms have been taken,"
 the innkeeper said.
"But I don't mind if you sleep in the stable,
 with the cow and the donkey."

That night, when darkness had fallen,
Mary's baby was born.

She wrapped him in a blanket and laid him in a manger.
"His name is Jesus," she said.

Out on the hillside, above the town,
the shepherds were fast asleep.
Heavenly music woke them!

Angels were singing a marvellous song!
"Glory to God in the highest!" they sang.
"And on earth peace, goodwill to all men."

The shepherds were frightened.
"What's happening? Who are you?" they said.
"Don't be afraid," the angels replied.
"We bring you good news."

"The Saviour, Christ the Lord, has been born.
You'll find him in a stable, lying in a manger."
The shepherds looked at each other.
"We'll go at once to look for him," they said.

So they hurried to Bethlehem,
and found the stable,
and saw Mary and Joseph,

and the baby, lying in the manger.
And putting down their lambs,
they knelt and adored him.

Far away, in distant lands, three wise men looked
up at the sky and saw a bright new star.

"A king has been born!" they all said,
and they set off on the long journey to find him.

They came to Jerusalem to the palace of King Herod.
"Where is the child who is born to be king?"
they said. "We have seen his star in the east
and have come to worship him."

Herod was angry when he heard this.
"I am the king!" he thought.
"This child must die!"

He called his counsellors.
"Where will Christ be born?" he asked them.
"In Bethlehem," they said.
So Herod said to the wise men,

"Look for the child in Bethlehem,
   and tell me when you have found him."
Secretly he said to himself,
And when I know where he is, I will kill him.

The three wise men saw that Herod's heart was wicked.
"When we find the child, we'll keep his place a secret,"
they said to each other.

They travelled on, resting by day
and following the star by night
until they came to Bethlehem.

At last they found the place where Jesus was.
They bowed down and worshipped him

and gave him their gifts,
gold, frankincense and myrrh.

And Mary, holding the baby in her arms,
remembered all these things,
and pondered them in her heart.